Duration 30 Min.

ANTONIO VIVALDI
(1678 - 1741)
GLORIA

for Solo Voices, Mixed Chorus and Orchestra

Elaboration by
ALFREDO CASELLA

Piano Reduction by
MAFFEO ZANON

English Version by
JOSEPH MACHLIS

I. Gloria

*)Orchestral materials on rental

sis De _ _o.
HIGH, GLO - - RY.

sis De _ _o.
HIGH, GLO - - RY.

sis De _ _o.
HIGH, GLO - - RY.

sis De _ _o.
HIGH, GLO - - RY.

Glo _ ri_a, glo _ ri_a in ex cel _ _ _
GLO - RI—OUS, GLO - RI—OUS, GLO — RY IN THE

Glo _ ri_a, glo _ ri_a in ex cel _ _ _
GLO - RI—OUS, GLO - RI—OUS, GLO — RY IN THE

Glo _ ri_a, glo _ ri_a in ex cel _ _ _
GLO - RI—OUS, GLO - RI—OUS, GLO — RY IN THE

Glo _ ri_a, glo _ ri_a in ex cel _ _ _
GLO - RI—OUS, GLO - RI—OUS, GLO — RY IN THE

II. Et in terra pax hominibus

III. Laudamus te

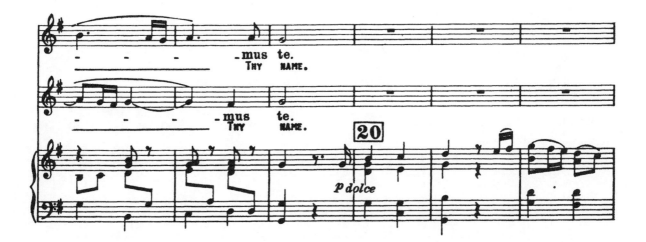

IV. Gratias agimus tibi

Soprani

Gra _ ti _ as a _ gi _ mus ti _ bi, gra _ ti _ as a _ gi _ mus ti _ bi.
LORD, WE A - DORE THEE, WE BLESS THEE; LORD WE A - DORE THEE, WE BLESS THEE.

Contralti

Gra _ ti _ as a _ gi _ mus ti _ bi, gra _ ti _ as a _ gi _ mus ti _ bi.
LORD, WE A - DORE THEE, WE BLESS THEE; LORD WE A - DORE THEE, WE BLESS THEE.

Tenori

Gra _ ti _ as a _ gi _ mus ti _ bi, gra _ ti _ as a _ gi _ mus ti _ bi.
LORD, WE A - DORE THEE, WE BLESS THEE; LORD WE A - DORE THEE, WE BLESS THEE.

Bassi

Gra _ ti _ as a _ gi _ mus ti _ bi, gra _ ti _ as a _ gi _ mus ti _ bi.
LORD, WE A - DORE THEE, WE BLESS THEE; LORD WE A - DORE THEE, WE BLESS THEE.

Adagio

V. Propter magnam gloriam

VI. Domine Deus

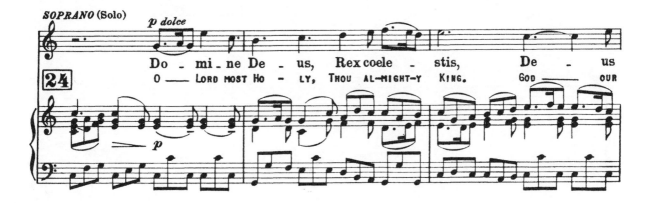

De _ us Pa _ ter, De _ us,　Rex＿＿ coele _ _ _

Thou al-might-y, Fa-ther,　Thou ＿ most ho-

_ _ _ stis,　Pa _ ter omni _ potens.

_ _ _ ly,　O Thou most ho- ly King.

26

Do _ mi _ ne De_us, Do _ mi _ ne De_us, Rex coele _ stis.

O ＿ Lord most ho- ly, O ＿ Lord most ho-ly, Thou al-might-y King,

p dolce

De _ us Pa_ter, De_us Pa_ter,　Pa_ _ _ _ ter, Pa_

God our Fa-ther, God our Fa-ther,　Fa_ _ _ _ -ther, O

_ter omni _ potens,
LORD OM-NI -PO-TENT.

Pa_
FA -

27

_ _ _ter, Pa_ter omni _ potens.
- -THER, O LORD OM-NI - PO-TENT.

28

poco allarg.

VII. Domine Fili Unigenite

32

34

VIII. Domine Deus, Agnus Dei

Do _ mi _ ne _ De _ us, Do _ mi _ ne De _ us, A _ gnus
LORD, GOD AL _ MIGHT _ Y, LORD, GOD AL _ MIGHT _ Y, LAMB OF

_ca _ ta,
GRESS _ IONS.

_ca _ ta,
GRESS _ IONS.

_ca _ ta,
GRESS _ IONS.

_ca _ ta,
GRESS _ IONS.

De _ i, Fi _ li _ us Pa _ tris, mi _ se _ re _ re,
GOD, OUR BLESS _ ED RE _ DEEM _ ER LORD HAVE MER _ CY,

f Qui tol _ lis pec _ ca _ ta mun _ di.
O GRANT EV _ ER _ LAST _ ING MER _ CY

f Qui tol _ lis pec _ ca _ ta mun _ di.
O GRANT EV _ ER _ LAST _ ING MER _ CY

f Qui tol _ lis pec _ ca _ ta mun _ di.
O GRANT EV _ ER _ LAST _ ING MER _ CY

f Qui tol _ lis pec _ ca _ ta mun _ di.
O GRANT EV _ ER _ LAST _ ING MER _ CY

f Qui tol _ lis pec _ ca _ ta mun _ di.
O GRANT EV _ ER _ LAST _ ING MER _ CY

IX. Qui tollis peccata mundi

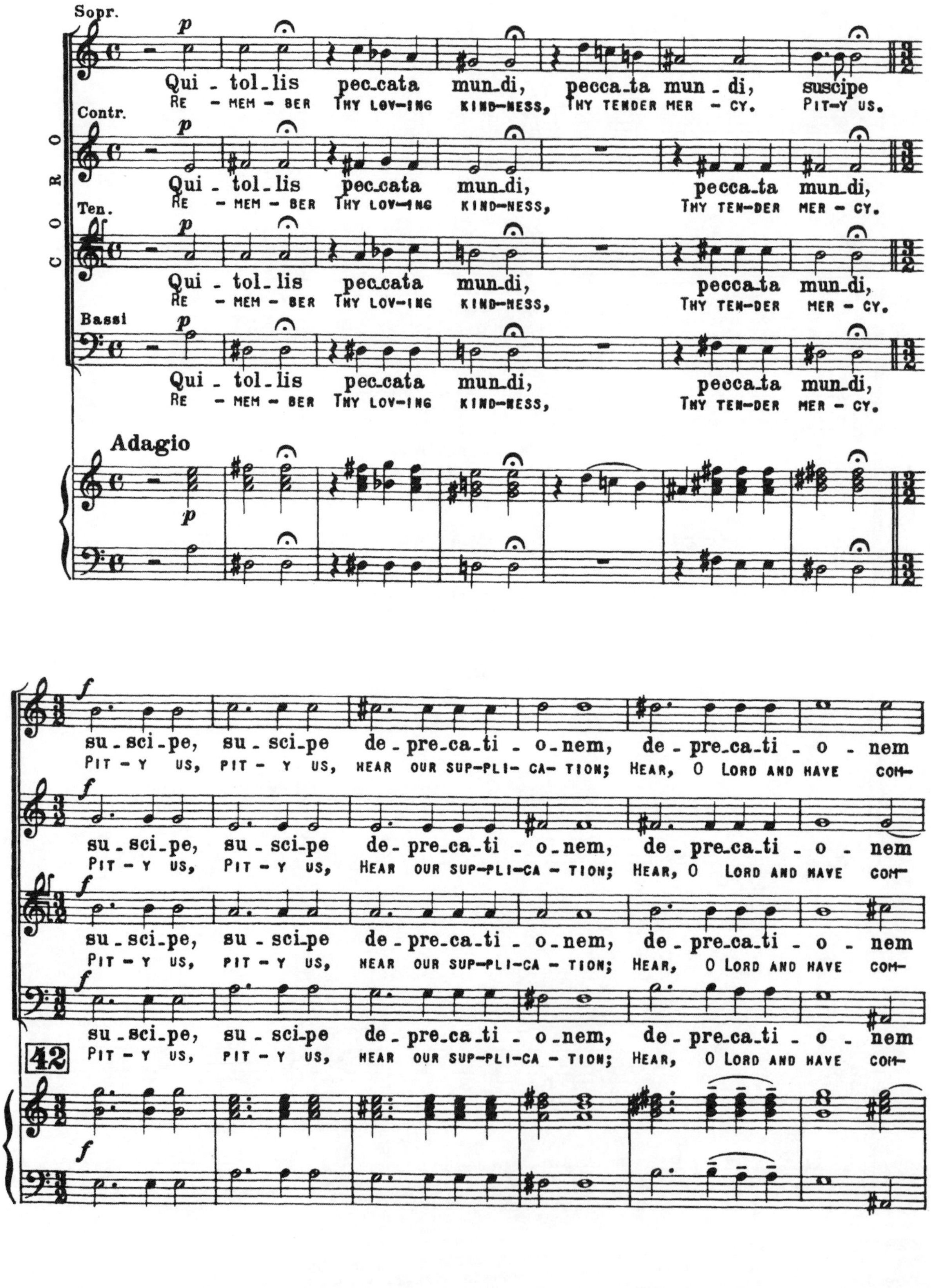

no - stram, de - pre - cati - o - nem no - stram.
PAS - SION. HEAR, O LORD AND HAVE COM - PAS - SION.

— no - stram, de - preca - ti - o - nem — no - stram.
— PAS - SION. HEAR, O LORD AND HAVE COM - - - PAS - - - SION.

no - stram, de - preca - ti - o - nem no - stram.
PAS - SION. HEAR, O LORD AND HAVE COM - PAS - SION.

no - stram, de - preca - ti - o - nem no - stram.
PAS - SION. HEAR, O LORD AND HAVE COM - PAS - - - - SION.

X. Qui sedes ad dexteram

CONTRALTO (Solo)

44

sempre f

Qui se -
DE - LIV -

p

- - - des   ad   dex - - - teram Pa - tris,
- - - ER   THY PEO - - - PLE FROM E - VIL.

p

p

meno p

mi - se - re - - - -
HAVE COM - PAS - - - -

mp

re, mi _ se _ re _ re, mi _ se _ re _ re

_ sion. Lord have mer - cy, Lord have mer - cy

no _ bis.

on us.

45

Qui se _ des ad dexteram Pa _ tris,

De _ liv - _ er Thy peo-ple from e - vil.

XI. Quoniam tu solus Sanctus

XII. Cum Sancto Spiritu

in glo ri a De i Pa tris, De i Patris. A men.
Thou MIGHT Y AND EV ER LAST ING GOD IN HEAVEN A MEN.

A men. A men. A men.
A MEN. A MEN. A MEN.

men.
MEN.

Spi ri tu, in gloria De i Patris, in gloria De i Pa tris. A men.
POWERFUL AND GLORIOUS AND EV ER LAST ING, OM NI PO TENT GOD IN HEAV EN A MEN.

espress. mf

54

Ten.

p dolce

Cum San cto Spi ri
GLO RIOUS AND POW ER

Bassi

p dolce A

55

(marcato, ma sempre dolce)

glo_ri_a De_i Pa_tris. A _ men.
NI-PO-TENT GOD IN HEAV-EN. A - MEN.

_ men.
- MEN.

_ men.
- MEN.

glo_ri_a De_i Patris. A _ men.
THOU MIGHT-Y GOD IN HEAV-EN A - MEN.

56

f subito

A _ men.
A - - MEN.

Cum Sancto Spi _ ri_tu, in
GLO - RIOUS AND POW - ER-FUL, OM-

A _ men.
A- -MEN. *f*

Cum Sancto
FOR THOU ART

57

marcato

Cum San - cto Spi - ri - tu, in glo - ri - a De - i Pa - tris.
GLO - RIOUS AND POW - ER-FUL OM - NI - PO - TENT GOD IN HEAV - EN
glo - ri - a De - i Pa - tris. A - - men. A -
NI - PO - TENT GOD IN HEAV - EN A - - MEN. A -
A - - men. A - men.
A - - MEN. A - MEN.
Spi - ri - tu, in glo - ri - a De - i Patris. A - men. Cum Sancto Spi - ri - tu, in glo - ri - a De - i
POW - ER - FUL OM - NI - PO - TENT GOD IN HEAV - EN, A - MEN, FOR THOU ART POW - ER - FUL OM - NI - PO - TENT GOD IN
A - men. A - - men. A - men. A - - men.
A - MEN. A - - - MEN. A - MEN. A - - MEN.
- men. A - - men. A - - men. A -
- - MEN. A - - MEN. A - - - MEN. A -
A - men. A - men. A - men. A - men. A - men.
A - MEN. A - MEN. A - MEN. A - MEN. A - MEN.
Pa - tris. A - - men. A - - men. A -
HEAV - EN. A - - MEN. A - - MEN. A -
(tr)

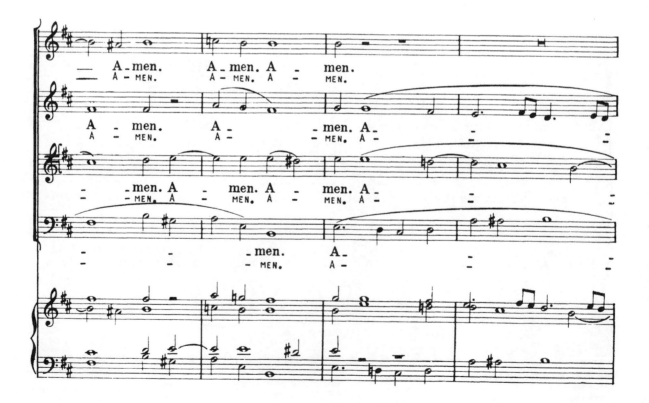